GW00360093

ACCESS DENIED:
DILBERT'S QUEST FOR
LOVE IN THE NINETIES

ACCESS DENIED:
DILBERT'S QUEST FOR
LOVE IN THE NINETIES

A DILBERT™ BOOK
BY
SCOTT ADAMS

B◉XTREE

First published in 1996 by Andrews and McMeel, a Universal Press Syndicate Company,
4900 Main Street, Kansas City, Missouri, 64112, USA

This edition published in 1997 by Boxtree,
an imprint of Macmillan Publishers Ltd,
25 Eccleston Place, London, SW1W 9NF
and Basingstoke

Associated companies throughout the world

ISBN 0 7522 2421 2

Copyright © 1996 by United Feature Syndicate, Inc.

All rights reserved. No part of this publication may be
reproduced, stored in or introduced into a retrieval system, or
transmitted, in any form, or by any means (electronic, mechanical,
photocopying, recording or otherwise) without the prior written
permission of the publisher. Any person who does any unauthorized
act in relation to this publication may be liable to criminal
prosecution and civil claims for damage.

3 5 7 9 8 6 4 2

A CIP catalogue record for this book is available from the British Library

Printed in Singapore

This book is sold subject to the condition that it shall not,
by way of trade or otherwise, be lent, hired out, re-sold,
or otherwise circulated without the publisher's prior consent
in any form of binding or cover other than that in which
it is published and without a similar condition including this
condition being imposed on the subsequent purchaser.

ACCESS DENIED:
DILBERT'S QUEST FOR
LOVE IN THE NINETIES

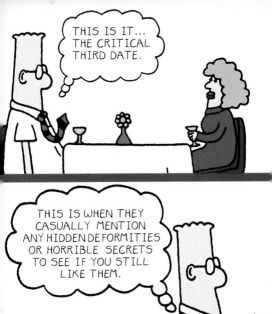

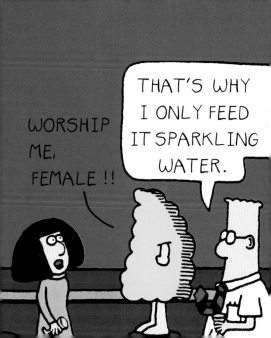

I'M TALKING ABOUT NEXT WEEK !!
I DON'T THINK I COULD HAVE ANOTHER BITE. ALL FULL.

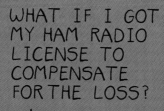

I'M SO LUCKY TO BE DATING YOU, LIZ. YOU'RE AT LEAST AN EIGHT.
YOU'RE A TEN.